CONTENTS

THE EDUCATIONAL AND EMOTIONAL ADJUSTMENTS OF STUTTERING CHILDREN

CHAPTER I

THE PROBLEM

This study recounts an attempt to understand more fully the nature of stuttering and its possible effects upon those afflicted with this speech difficulty.

"Stuttering" is here defined as an intermittent inability to produce voiced sounds accompanied by severe cramps of the diaphragm, larynx, tongue, or all three of these speech organs. It is recognized by the following symptoms, more or less frequently present: (1) repetition of consonant sounds preceding vowels; (2) inability to speak words, phrases, or sentences beginning with vowels; (3) special difficulty in emitting short vowels; (4) tics, or muscular spasms of the face, particularly blinking of the eyes; (5) general muscular tension throughout the body, exhibited in clenched hands and toes; (6) glottal catches; (7) back placement of the vowels; (8) irregular, jerky grouping of phrases; (9) lack of rhythm; (10) gasping breath controlled in its emission by the muscles of the larynx.

The symptom essentially differentiating stuttering from similar speech defects is the laryngeal cramp. [1: pp. 10 ff.; 2: p. 278][1] "Cluttering" is most frequently confused with stuttering because of its rapid, hasty, jerky, arhythmic grouping of phrases and repetition of consonants and vowels, but cluttering does not have the hypertension of the throat muscles. [1: p. 46] "Aphonia" is like stuttering in that it is an inability to produce voice; it is unlike stuttering in that it is a chronic condition, occurring consistently on all voiced sounds, while stuttering is intermittent, or occurring at spasmodic intervals, and upon various voiced sounds, sometimes one, sometimes another. [3: pp. 181 ff.] Moreover,

[1] The number within brackets refer to the item bearing that number in the Bibliography on page 59.

aphonia is not always accompanied by hypertonicity of the muscles of the throat. [1: p. 49]   Mild motor aphasias resemble
stuttering in the hesitation upon words or syllables, but possess
a more general hesitation on both voiced and unvoiced sounds and
show no evidence of cramps of the muscles which control the
organs used in producing voice.   [1: pp. 50ff.]

"Stammering" is frequently used to designate the speech disorder called "stuttering," but the term "stammering" has been
used so generally as identical with lisping (mutilated speech)· or
with one phase of stuttering (the repetition of consonants) or
with various other voice inadequacies, that it has ceased to have
any practical value as exact definition.   [3: p. 181]

Much has been written and said about the causes and cures
for stuttering. Recently emotional phases have received particular stress, especially observations that often stuttering is present
most frequently and severely in social conversation rather than
in talking to oneself, and that it seems to become increasingly
troublesome in times of emotional stress and social pressure.
Consequently we have methods and programs for cures based
upon "emotional reëducation" or "mental reëducation" in con-
trast to the former practices established on the hypothesis that
"stuttering is due to permanent anatomical anomalies which were
amenable to surgical treatment." [4: pp. 191-97]

"Then wedge-shaped portions were cut from the back of the
tongue; the hypoglossal nerve, the lingual frenum, and the various extrinsic and intrinsic muscles of the tongue were severed.
The tongue was pierced with needles, cauteries, blisters, and
embrocations of petroleum, also inoculations of croton oil were
administered. Tincture of rectified alcohol, peppermint oil, and
chloroform were applied. Wooden wedges were placed between
the teeth. Smoking was recommended as a sedative to the vocal
cords. These and various other remedies were devised on the
assumption that the difficulty was organic and peripheral." [5:
p. 205 quoting from 4]

"Later this hypothesis was supplanted by the theory that
although the difficulty is not caused by gross anomalies, yet a
permanent impairment of the nervous system is present. Kutz-
man in *Die Storungen der Sprache* holds consistently to the view
that stuttering is a 'spastic coördination neurosis.' This view is
adhered to by modern writers, especially those who approach the

subject from a medical point of view. Gutzman holds that every stutterer is neuropathically afflicted. E. W. Scripture claims that 'stuttering is a distinct form of nervous disease, it can be properly and legally treated only by a physician.' " [5: p. 205]

Recently, however, even medical practitioners look upon stuttering as a "psychological problem." "Many persons stammer (stutter) under certain conditions largely because they think they will. All their past experiences with speech have combined to confirm them in the thought and it soon becomes a sort of 'fixed idea.' " [Makuen]

"Langwill believes stammering (stuttering) is essentially a functional affection—a neurosis, the result of the defective working of the complex coördinated mechanism concerned in the production of speech, and not a defect of structure. Pathological lesions, therefore, need not be looked for. Gutzman, in spite of his belief that every stutterer is neuropathically afflicted, also holds that in the psychology of stuttering we do not find the destruction of any separate fibres or special centres; also the connection between the sensory centre and the ideational centres on the one hand, and the motor centre on the other are undisturbed. The stutterer simply does not succeed in making the coördination from the motor centre to the organs well enough to produce the correct mutual functioning.' " [5: pp. 205-6]

The Blantons consider stuttering as "the most serious defect of speech" and "as always superimposed on the neurotic constitution or temperament." They also hold that therapy should "aim at the reëducation of the temperament which remains virtually constant in its character." [6: pp. 100-1]

English Bagby distinguishes thus between stuttering and stammering: "In stammering there is a periodic arrest of the speech process and [it] is organic in origin. Stuttering is functional and consists in a repetition of syllables." He concludes that "timidity is the basis of the disturbance. Timidity is a mild form of fear. The fear basis of the disturbance is shown also by the fact that the severity of stuttering varies with the degree of the fear, or timidity. . . . Fear accounts for the maintenance of stuttering. . . . It is still necessary to account for the origin of stuttering as a habit." [7: Lecture 11]

Knight Dunlap's theory of the origin of stuttering also recognizes fear as a potent factor in the acquisition of this habit. "The idea is that the boy develops a street-corner vocabulary not appropriate to the fireside. In the presence of his parents he starts to use an obscene word, reacts with fear, and interrupts the word. Fear becomes attached to the syllable, and the fear always interferes with its use." [7: Lectures 11 and 8]

A desire to know more about these "psychological" and "mental" aspects of stuttering prompted the investigation which is the basis of this study. Some of the questions which seemed significant are:

1. Do stuttering children vary from normal children in intelligence? If so, is this variability more noticeable in language or non-language activities?

2. How do these children compare with non-stuttering children of like intelligence in their school achievement? Are there any appreciable differences in language abilities other than speech?

3. Are speech difficulties other than stuttering more prevalent among those children than among similar but non-stuttering children?

4. Are stuttering children apparently more emotionally unstable and socially maladjusted than similar but non-stuttering children?

5. Are marked physical abnormalities present more frequently among stuttering than among non-stuttering children?

CHAPTER II

THE PROCEDURE

The equivalent-groups type of experimental procedure offered the most discriminating opportunities for making these comparisons because of the possibilities of judging the realities of the differences between stutterers and the control group. [9: p. 29]

Seven schools in New York City representing patrons of different types of economic and social background and of racial inheritance were canvassed for stutterers. All children showing symptoms of speech defects were reported by their teachers or by the teacher of Speech Improvement. They were examined by the writer, and those exhibiting the type of speech difficulty hitherto described as "stuttering" became the experimental group.

A control group equivalent in chronological age, mental age, intelligence (as determined by the Stanford Revision of the Binet Intelligence Test), sex, and language and racial background was selected by matching each stutterer with a non-stuttering child who had similar ranking in each of these considerations. Although this matching technique was difficult and time consuming, it justified itself in view of the fact that so many tests and comparisons were contemplated.

Both groups were then subjected to the following testing program and the data compiled for a comparison of the two groups on the various counts:

1. Pintner-Patterson Shorter Performance Scale.
2. Stanford Achievement Tests.
3. Woodworth-Matthews Questionnaire.
4. Woodworth-Cady Questionnaire.
5. Kent-Rosanoff Free Association Test.
6. Wood-Rowell Health and Growth Examination.
7. A special test for correct pronunciation of vowels and consonants devised by the experimenter.
8. The scale for judging personality traits used by Terman in his study of exceptionally bright children. [10: pp. 523ff.]

CHAPTER III

INTELLIGENCE

I. INCIDENCE

Out of a total enrollment of 7,138 pupils in the seven schools chosen for the experiment, 62 children showing varying degrees of the severity of the stuttering cramps were found. One of these was dropped out of the computations because his parents objected to his "being experimented upon." The remaining 61 registered intelligence quotients on the Stanford Revision of the Binet Intelligence Test ranging from 63 to 156. The mean of the distribution fell at 99.14 with a value of 20.3 for the standard deviation. The group is practically typical according to the norms for the test.

The incidence of stuttering, as we have found it, is hardly comparable to results obtained in similar studies because we cannot be sure other investigations limited the diagnosis as was done in this experiment, nor that our 7,138 school children were a representative sampling of school children in general. However, comparisons may be at least interesting. The percentage of the population of the seven schools having symptoms of stuttering sufficiently evident to be noticed by the teachers or by the speech correction teacher was .87 per cent. All children who had shown any sort of speech difficulty were examined, and those exhibiting the symptoms we called stuttering were chosen as the experimental group. Smiley Blanton, who defines stuttering as it is understood in this study, found .72 per cent of the school population to be suffering from this difficulty. [10: p. 583] E. W. Scripture claims "statistics show from 1 to 2 per cent of stutterers among school children. A smaller percentage in the lower classes becomes trebled in the higher ones. Marked increases are found at the periods of second dentition and puberty." [1: p. 9] Wallin found .7 per cent. [12: p. 219] Conradi in a survey of 87,440 school children found .87 per cent. [13: p. 365] Root found stutterers and stammerers make up 1.2 per cent of the

6

school population. He defines stuttering and stammering thus: "the most obvious signs are continuous or interrupted spasms of the organs of respiration, phonation or articulation." [14: p. 533] Danish children investigated by Westergaard showed .61 per cent; Lingberg found .9 per cent for Danish country children and .74 per cent for city children. Don Sarbo reported 1.02 per cent of 231,000 children in the towns of Hungary, and Rouma 1.4 per cent of 14,235 children in the cities of Belgium. Wallin gives the average of seven of these surveys as .9 per cent with the extremes ranging from a little over one-half per cent to about one and a half per cent. [12: p. 214]

The question of sex has been a conspicuous factor in the incidence of stuttering, boys always outnumbering girls. In the survey made for this study boys outnumbered girls 2.9 to 1. These figures must be considered as suggestive rather than conclusive, in view of the fact that the proportion of boys to girls in the total group is not known. Other investigations report the excess of boy stutterers over girl stutterers as 4 or 5 to 1 [Bluemel—3: p. 210]; from 2 to 1 to 9 to 1 [Scripture—1: p. 9]; 3 to 1 [Blanton—10: p. 584]; 3 to 1 [Conradi—13: p. 365]; 2.2 to 1 [Root—14: p. 537]; 2.8 to 1 [Wallin—12: p. 215].

Whether these 7,138 school children are a group representative of the school population of New York City cannot be determined, as it was not practical to give Binet Intelligence Tests to each individual. The children came from schools having various types of patrons in approximately the following proportions:

1. Public School—negro, Irish, Jewish tenement dwellers, poor laboring class—6.7 — per cent.
2. Public School—negro, Italian, Porto Rican, Irish, Jewish laboring class, poor tenements—28. + per cent.
3. Public School—very mixed and polyglot group, largely Jewish "upper middle class," some Irish of skilled labor group—33.7 + per cent.
4. Public School—largely rich Jewish clientele, some middle-class Irish— 23.8 + per cent.
5 and 6. Two private schools patronized largely by "American" families, of British origin for the most part, and having about 20 per cent Jewish children—7.6 — per cent.
7. A Cardiac class in an Italian Settlement House, almost entirely Italian in patrons—.3 per cent.

The occupations of the parents as far as we could determine in interviews with the subjects of both groups were as follows.

Occupation of Parent	Stutterers	Control
Lawyer	1	1
Physician and Surgeon	–	1
Manufacturer	1	4
Merchant—owner and manager	9	5
Merchant—clerk	3	3
Engineer—"Professional"	1	1
Actor	2	–
"Public Service"	–	1
Insurance—executive	–	1
Theater	–	1
Salesman—bonds, real estate, etc.	2	6
Skilled labor—steel construction, etc.	8	3
Unskilled labor—garbage collectors, etc.	6	6
Motorman	1	2
"Moving"	1	2
Watchman	1	–
Barber	2	–
Manager of Restaurant—head waiter, etc.	4	1
Domestic Service	1	–
Superintendent of Apartment House	1	6
Chauffeur	1	1
Policeman or Detective	1	1
Unreported	2	2
Dead—or charge of charity institution	2	2

Should we accept this sample as reasonably representative of school children in general, we may interpret the results of the Binet Intelligence Test scores as indicating that stuttering children show up as well as any other random sampling on an intelligence scale largely weighted with language tests. This group fell within one point of the standardized average with approximately 68 per cent of the group lying within twenty points each side of that point.

II. RATINGS ON LANGUAGE AND NON-LANGUAGE INTELLIGENCE TESTS

Difficulties in equating the experimental and control groups as well as numerous absences due to epidemics of colds and scarlet fever reduced the numbers used in the various studies. Consequently it was necessary to reëquate the groups for each set of data. Matching stutterers with non-stutterers in racial and language background presented special difficulties because of the mixed inheritance of some of the group. Two cases where one parent was Japanese and the other Scotch or Swiss were matched with non-stuttering children coming from English and English-French parents where French was spoken at home, because the latter tongue was spoken in the Japanese homes. In both of these cases the subjects reported that practically no Japanese was spoken or understood by them. Special care was taken in matching children speaking Jewish and German dialects with like non-stutterers. Popular opinion has often intimated that Jewish children stutter more frequently than children of other parentage because of the emotional results of the persecutions of their ancestors. The experimenter had often suspected the back-placement of the vowels and the use of the glottal stop (two symptoms frequently found in exaggerated degree in stutterers, and common to German dialects) of being conducive to stuttering, and was anxious to eliminate this factor and thus avoid undue influence on the results of the experiments.

Racial and language inheritance for the two groups was:

Jewish—stutterers, 18; control, 18.
British (English, Scotch, Irish, American)—stutterers, 20; control, 22.
(One stutterer was of Japanese-Scotch ancestry.)
Romance (Spanish, Greek, French, Italian)—stutterers, 6; control, 8.
(One stutterer was of Japanese-Swiss-French parentage.)
German, Danish, Dutch—stutterers, 7; control, 3.
Negro—stutterers, 2; control, 2.

The apparent discrepancy between the number of German, Danish, Dutch, is probably not a real one in view of the fact that the three Danish children used mostly English and were matched with English-speaking children, and that one child of English ancestry was matched with a child speaking French, because French was the language used in the home.

When the experimental and control groups had been equated, they showed intelligence quotients having a difference of only .1 point between the means. Only fifty children were included in each group. The mean I.Q. for the experimental group was 101.9; that for the control 102.0. The variability of the former gave a value of 19.87 to the standard deviation; that of the latter a value of 20.26. The mental ages for the experimental group had a mean of 122.6 with standard deviation equal to 25.58; the control, **123.2**, with standard deviation equal to **26.34**. The two groups were therefore considered equated on those counts. [9: p. 58; p. 46]

Results of the Pintner-Patterson Shorter Performance Scale testing gave a mean I.Q. of 104.2 with the standard deviation valued at 26.73 for stutterers; and 99.8 with standard deviation valued at 23.0 for the control group. The obtained difference was 4.4 in favor of the experimental group. The reliability of this difference is so small that we cannot be sure we have a real difference. The experimental coefficient is equal to only .317, which, interpreted in terms of chances, means about 3.9 to 1 that we have a real difference. A coefficient of 1.0 would mean just exactly practical certainty according to McCall. [11: pp. 404-5]

Two Binet tests dealing largely with language abilities were selected for special comparison. These were the Free Association Test at the ten-year level and the Vocabulary Test which asks for a knowledge of the meanings of words.

Results of the comparisons on both were negative. In the Free Association Test when the subject was asked to name as many words as he could think of within three minutes, the stutterers, in spite of the blockage in enunciation, showed a mean of 69.1665 as compared to the control mean score of 69.7220. The standard deviation for the former was 26.77; that for the latter 20.56. The experimental coefficient was equal to .04.

In the Vocabulary Test the stutterers had a mean score of 31.2448, the control of 30.551. The standard deviation in the former case was 12.08; in the latter 13.43. The experimental coefficient was .097.

These differences can be appreciated when we consider that an experimental coefficient of .1 is equal to a chance for a difference of only 1.6 to 1, and that 1.0 means, roughly speaking, practical certainty.

Only forty-five pairs of subjects were used in the Free Association computations because the test was not included in their examination, the subject reaching a basal mental age either above or below it. Forty-nine pairs were used in the Vocabulary compilations for the same reason.

CHAPTER IV

SCHOOL ACHIEVEMENT

Speech defects, especially stuttering, are considered to have a very unwholesome effect upon school achievement. Blanton says, "Many children are so retarded in their school work by their speech defect that they drop out as soon as they reach the age when the law allows them to stop school." "In the case of the stutterers, even though the symptom be recovered from, there remains, in many cases, the original mental conflict, the lack of adjustment that causes other neurotic symptoms beside stuttering." [10: p. 585]

Root claims that "when measured according to over-ageness, it has been shown that speech defectives who remain in school are on the average six months older, or six months behind the average pupils without speech disorders. In terms of actual school progress, on the other hand, the retardation is considerably greater, on the average amounting to between ten and eleven months. Speech defectives generally make less progress through school in a given length of time than do average pupils, or pupils without defective speech. The extent of retardation increases from Grade I to Grade IV, after which elimination of those most retarded takes place." [15: p. 256]

The results of the standard achievement tests given both groups in this study did not support these opinions. In fact, they show no really appreciable difference between the accomplishment quotients of these two groups.

Only forty-five cases were available for this study because of illness of the pupils at the time of testing, and because of the fact that some of the subjects were not able to read well enough to take the test, having had less than one year of school experience.

The mean for the accomplishment quotients (educational age divided by mental age) for the stutterers was 100. with a standard deviation of 12.64; that for the control group 103.068 with a standard deviation of 12.67. The obtained difference between

11

the two was 3.068 and the experimental coefficient .408. Interpreted in terms of chances, this means less than half certainty that the difference is a real one and did not arise from the chances of experimentation. The chances are really about 65 to 1; McCall puts 369 to 1 as the point of practical certainty.

An inspection of the results of the individual tests making up the group using the Stanford Achievement Tests showed the following coefficients of experimentation:

Chronological age—.0029 in favor of experimental group, indicating that there was no difference and that equating on this point was accurate.
Mental age—.008 in favor of control group.
Intelligence Quotient—.02 in favor of control. The group was chosen with the purpose of making these coefficients as small as possible. In reading tests the coefficient was .17—less than 2.5 to 1. An analysis of the three different types of reading tests showed:

> Paragraph meaning ...........................E.C. .16
> Sentence meaning ...........................E.C. .22
> Word meaning ...............................E.C. .12

In arithmetic the coefficient was .22, with .25 for computation and .18 for reasoning. Spelling differences gave a coefficient of .19. In no case were the results better than chance.

CHAPTER V

EMOTIONAL AND SOCIAL ADJUSTMENTS

Three attempts to compare the emotional and social adjustments of the stutterers with those of the control group were made by giving each child (1) a combination of the Woodworth-Matthews and Woodworth-Cady questionnaires for identifying individuals with psychotic tendencies, (2) the Kent-Rosanoff Free Association Test, and (3) a teacher's rating on the basis of the trait inventory used by Terman in his study of gifted children. [16: p. 523]

I. WOODWORTH-MATTHEWS AND WOODWORTH-CADY QUESTIONNAIRES

The procedure in applying the questionnaires was not the standardized one of group testing. Instead, the writer gave each child an individual interview, using all but one of the questions on both questionnaires as a basis. The query, "Do you feel that your parents are not really your own?" was omitted at the request of the vice-principal of one of the schools canvassed for subjects. A few additional questions were introduced:

"Do you ever imagine people are talking about you behind your back?"
"What do you imagine they say?"
"Does it bother you very much?"
"Were you ever punished when you thought you didn't deserve it?"
"What did you do about it?"
"How long did it bother you?"
"Have you ever been so angry with a person that you thought you would never forgive him?"
"What did you do about it?"
"What do you do to 'pay back' people when you find you cannot vent your anger in word or deed?"

The enquirer had already established an acquaintance with the subject by means of five or six hours of testing given previously. She explained that she had with her some more questions about the way people feel about certain things in life, and that she was

13

desirous of finding out whether all the boys and girls who had been taking all of these tests recently felt the same way about these questions. Instead of giving just a "yes" and "no" answer each child was urged to "tell me all you can about this." His responses were taken down verbatim to be used in comparing the reactions of each group in all questions showing any great differences in the frequency of replies said to indicate psychotic tendencies.

The inventory of the combination of the two questionnaires supplemented by those mentioned above contained 120 questions. They were gathered from the report of Miss Matthews' study [17: p. 1-40] and from Terman's investigation of gifted children, wherein he reproduces Cady's list with a few modifications [16: p. 501].

The mean of the "psychotic" responses of the stuttering group fell at 22.6522 with a standard deviation of 9.616; that for the control at 20.1304 with a standard deviation of 9.9532. The experimental coefficient is .44, something less than half certainty that the testing showed a real difference between the two types of children.

Only forty-six pairs of subjects were included in the compilations because of casualties from the original fifty, due to absences from school. An analysis of the differences on the various questions was unfruitful in indicating any bias on the part of either group. Whether the devices used to select two groups equivalent in intelligence and racial heritage also selected children similar in emotional tendencies, we cannot tell.

The greatest difference on any one question was 11, with 22 unfavorable responses by stutterers and 11 by the controls. Other differences between the number of unfavorable responses large enough to be treated statistically for the reliability of the differences were:

STUTTERERS	CONTROL	DIFFERENCE
18	9	9
23	14	9
21	13	8
17	9	8

When these figures are examined for the reliability of the differences between proportions or per cents we have no appreciable bias indicated for either group. Most of the differences were so small that they made the formula unusuable. [18: pp. 254-62]

The standard deviation of a proportion or per cent $= \sqrt{\dfrac{PQ}{N}}$:

[18: p. 262] In the case of the unfavorable responses reported above the following results were obtained:

Group	No. of Unfavorable Responses	S.D. of Per Cent of Stutterers	S.D. of Per Cent of Controls	S.D. of Difference	Obtained Difference	S.D. of Difference	Experimental Coefficient
a. Stutterers...	22	.0728		.09522	.24	2.5205	.907
Control.....	11		.0614				
b. Stutterers...	18	.0708		.09102	.19	2.0877	.75
Control.....	9		.0572				
c. Stutterers...	23	.0729		.0989	.19	1.921	.69
Control.....	14		.0668				
d. Stutterers...	17	.0712		.0924	.17	1.840	.66
Control.....	9		.05897				
e. Stutterers...	7	.0526		.08705	—.18	—2.068	.74
Control.....	15		.0693				
f. Stutterers...	21	.0726		.0977	.17	1.74	.63
Control.....	13		.0655				

The nature of the questions which yielded these differences was:

a. "Do you get out of breath quickly when you run?"
b. "Does it make you uneasy to cross a bridge over water?"
   "Do you talk in your sleep?"
c. "Are your feelings often hurt so badly that you cry?"
d. "Are you bashful?"
e. "Do you have a hard time making up your mind about things?"
f. "Do you giggle a good deal and find you cannot help it?"

An interpretation of these figures leads one to suspect that stutterers admit that they "get out of breadth quickly when they run" more often than do non-stutterers, but in the case of the other questions there seems to be little difference between the two groups.

II. KENT-ROSANOFF FREE ASSOCIATION TEST

In the administering of the Kent-Rosanoff Free Association Test the standard list of words was used but additional words suggestive of alleged emotional undercurrents in stutterers reactions were interspersed, one after each fifth word of the standard list.

The procedure was that recommended by Rosanoff in his *Manual of Psychiatry.* [19: p. 547] The reaction time was taken to fifths of a second, and responses were scored according to the table of frequencies given there. The tables of Woodrow and Lowell for children's responses might have been more suitable for these subjects, but did not offer the same opportunity for detecting psychopathic responses, because they have not been so widely standardized or given to so many different types of individuals. The time reactions for each child were made into a distribution, and the mid-score and limits of the upper quartile were determined. A more accurate measure seemed useless expenditure of time and effort, because it involved splitting seconds, a measure much more exact than the stop watch and other crude testing conditions would exact. All words having reaction times falling beyond the normal curve of distribution were tabulated and inspected for any distinguishing habits between the two groups.

Comparisons of the two groups were made on the bases of the mid-scores, upper quartile points, excessive reaction times on particular words and on reaction times for the "key" words (those added to the standard list). These "key" words were: *unpopular, shame, speech, stammer, pet, love, hate, sweetheart, ill-mannered, afraid* (also in standard list), *punish, mad, crybaby, polite, slow-poke, stutter, bossy, lie, disgrace, hurry.* They were chosen because of popular notions that stuttering is a maladjustment due to shame, lack of social graces, an exaggerated desire to appear well in public, too much hurrying, "suppressed erotic desires," fears of every sort, browbeating on the part of those in authority, and similar disturbances.

Qualitative treatment of the responses yielded a classification of the replies into four general groups, as shown in the following list of categories:

Common Reactions
1. Specific.
2. Non-specific.

Doubtful
3. Doubtful.

Individual
 4. Sound reactions (neulogisms).
 5. Neulogisms without sound relation.
 6. Repetition of preceding reaction.
 7. Reaction repeated five times.
 8. Repetition of preceding stimulus.
 9. Derivatives.
10. Non-specific reactions.
11. Sound reactions (words).
12. Word complements.
13. Particles of speech.
14. Association to preceding stimulus.
15. Association to preceding reaction (by frequency tables).
16. Repetition of previous reaction.
17. Repetition of previous stimulus.
18. Normal by appendix.
19. Association to preceding reaction (without frequency tables).
20. Unclassified.

Failure to Respond
21. No reply.
22. "I don't know."
23. "What's that?"

Comparison of the means of the stutterers and controls was made according to the formulæ leading toward the determining of an experimental coefficient. "Key" words were treated similarly, except that "specific" responses became those common to both stutterers and controls; "doubtful," those representing only a grammatical variation from "common response"; and "individual," all others not included in "failure to respond." The latter consisted of such replies as: no answer, "I don't know that word," "What's that?" and the like.

Differences between the two groups in the mid-scores of the reaction times for the 120 words were negligible. The mean for stutterers fell at 2.8951 seconds (S.D. 1.164) and that for the controls at 2.6951 (S.D. .9228) with an experimental coefficient equal to .310. Means for the location of the upper quartiles were: stutterers, 4.6878 (S.D. 2.3064); and control, 4.1415 (S.D. 1.529) with an experimental coefficient of .455. In neither case does the difference seem equal to as much as "half certainty."

All words having reaction times of eight seconds or more were considered individually and compared for frequency of the occurrence of the prolonged pause before responses. Eight seconds was chosen as the minimum point from which to reckon these excessive reaction times, because in almost every case this point lay beyond the upper limits of the more or less normal curves of distribution for each individual's responses to the 120 stimulus words.

Examination of the differences between the number of times each word fell into the excessively long reaction group did reveal a mark of distinction between the stutterers and the controls (experimental coefficient, 1.3). In only four cases did one group delay responses beyond the eight-second limit more than five times in excess of the other group. These differences were treated statistically for the differences between proportions as follows:

WORD	NUMBER OF EXCESSIVE REACTION TIMES		S.D. OF PER CENT OF STUTTERERS	S.D. OF PER CENT OF CONTROLS	S.D. OF DIFFERENCE	OBTAINED DIFFERENCE	RATIO OF DIFF. TO S.D. OF DIFF.	EXPERIMENTAL COEFFICIENT
hand	Stutterers	7	.0587					
	Controls	2		.0340	.0678	.12	1.770	.64
rough	Stutterers	8	.0625					
	Controls	3		.0398	.07409	.13	1.755	.63
afraid	Stutterers	8	.0625					
	Controls	3		.0398	.07409	.13	1.755	.63
long	Stutterers	7						
	Controls	0	Per cent of controls too small to be treated statistically					
Total responses	Stutterers	428	.00408					
	Controls	366		.00363	.005466	.02	3.66	1.3

In spite of the habitual hesitation in speech processes, stutterers show little difference in their responses from those of the control group except in the case of excessively long reaction times.

Qualitative treatment of the results of the Kent-Rosanoff Free Association Test resolved itself into a comparison of the two groups in the frequencies with which they responded to the stimulus with common, doubtful, or individual reactions. "Failures to respond" were so few that they could not be treated by the formulæ for the reliability of a difference between proportions, in the case of stutterers 24 per cent, and among controls 35 per cent.

No distribution curve was possible because of the scarcity of cases.

The summary table in Chapter VIII gives a detailed report of the findings. A brief account will here point out that in common responses we have a mean of 69.2075 for stutterers and 70.427 for controls with respective standard deviations of 22.13 and 21.415. The experimental coefficient is less than .1, about .091, or almost exact equality for the two groups.

Doubtful responses gave a mean of 5.2317 (S.D. 4.0606) for stutterers and 4.256 (S.D. 3.707) for controls, with an experimental coefficient of .409, something less than half certainty. The same general conclusions can be drawn from the results of the individual responses where was found a mean of 25.6705 (S.D. 2155) for controls, with an experimental coefficient of .028 when a coefficient of 1.0 would indicate certainty of a real difference.

The only interpretation of these results which seems justified is that the Kent-Rosanoff Test does not reveal any distinctive traits which lie in stuttering children's emotional adaptations.

A study of the reaction times for the experimental and control groups on the "key" words showed no appreciable difference between stutterers and non-stutterers at either the location of the mid-score or the point of the upper quartile. The results can be summed up as follows:

Group	Mid-Scores	Upper Quartile
Experimental Group		
Mean	3.25	5.98
S.D. of Distribution	.632	1.6124
S.D. of Mean	.1413	.3634
Control Group		
Mean	3.17	5.36
S.D. of Distribution	.8816	1.8564
S.D. of Mean	.1971	.4151
Obtained Differences of Mean	.08	.62
S.D. of Difference of Mean	.24	.5517
Rates of Difference to S.D. of Difference	.3333	1.124
Experimental Coefficient	.12	.4

These differences are so small that they may easily have arisen out of chance variations in the conditions of testing. The "key" words have failed to bring to light any bias for either group in the way of lengthened reaction times for words supposed to be suggestive of particular emotional inadequacies of stutterers.

An examination of the reaction times lying far outside of the normal curve for each subject (8 seconds or more) gives the following information:

WORD	No. of Reaction Times in Excess of 8 Seconds		DIFFERENCE	IN FAVOR OF
	Experimentals	Controls		
Unpopular	11	12	1	Control
Shame	11	8	3	Experimental
Speech	2	2	0	
Stammer	4	6	2	Control
Pet	2	3	1	Control
Love	9	5	4	Experimental
Hate	7	6	1	Experimental
Sweetheart	4	4	0	
Ill-mannered	9	8	1	Experimental
Afraid	8	3	5	Experimental
Punish	3	7	4	Control
Mad	3	3	0	
Cry-baby	6	3	3	Experimental
Polite	4	4	0	
Slow-poke	6	7	1	Control
Stutter	8	4	4	Experimental
Bossy	6	6	0	
Lie	2	3	1	Control
Disgrace	2	3	1	Control
Hurry	3	1	2	Experimental

In studying the qualitative responses of these "key" words the statistical procedure of finding the reliability of the differences between two proportions was employed. The following tabulation summarizes the results:

GROUP	No. of Stimuli	Common Responses	Individual Responses	Doubtful Responses	Failure to Respond
Stutterers	820	380 (46%)	358 (44 %)	80 (9.8%)	2 (.2%)
Control	820	381 (46%)	376 (46—%)	63 (8 %)	....

Since the difference in any case is less than 2 per cent, the formula for judging the reliability of these differences gave no evidence of real difference. (Doubtful Responses, experimental coefficient = .51; Individual, .3.)

III. TRAIT RATINGS

One rating from the teacher was obtained for each child of both groups. In many cases several ratings were given by teachers whose acquaintance with the subjects dated back several years; but because of the possibility that disparity in numbers might unduly influence the results, only one teacher's opinions were used in interpreting the results.

The traits rated were those selected by Terman for his study of gifted children: (1) health; (2) amount of physical energy; (3) prudence and forethought; (4) self-confidence; (5) will-power and perseverance; (6) musical appreciation; (7) appreciation of beauty; (8) sense of humor; (9) cheerfulness and optimism; (10) permanency of moods; (11) fondness for large groups; (12) leadership; (13) popularity with other children; (14) sensitiveness to approval or disapproval; (15) desire to excel; (16) freedom from vanity and egotism; (17) sympathy and tenderness; (18) generosity and unselfishness; (19) conscientiousness; (20) truthfulness; (21) mechanical ingenuity; (22) desire to know; (23) originality; (24) common sense; (25) general intelligence. [16: p. 524]

Each teacher was asked to put a cross on the line accompanying each trait at the point which shows how much of that trait the child possesses. The middle of the line represented the average amount of the trait. The meanings of other points were stated carefully at seven intervals along the line. Each rater was asked to compare the child with the average child of the same age.

In compiling the results of the ratings, when there was doubt about the intention of the rater in the location of the cross, the writer was guided by the apparent habit of the rater in other judgments submitted. Thirteen points of location were used: 1; 1.5; 2; 2.5; 3; 3.5; 4; 4.5; 5; 5.5; 6; 6.5; 7. "Average" was at 4. Means for each group and standard deviations were computed. In the instances of largest differences the data were treated for the reliability of these differences. The following tabulation summarizes the results.

Equating the Groups	Mean M.A.	S.D.	Mean I.Q.	S.D.
Stutterers	123.2145	26.06	101.6665	20.025
Control	122.857	27.001	100.476	19.245

Note: See table below.

Inspection of these results shows differences which are very small in comparison with the variability, except in the case of trait 4, "self-confidence." Here the difference is .7482 and the S.D. of the difference .2339, giving an experimental coefficient of 1.15 certainty. This finding is quite in accord with the popular opinion that stutterers are shy, timid, and lacking in self-confidence.

Trait	Mean of Experimental Group	Mean of Control Group	Diff.	S.D. of Distribution Experimental Group	S.D. of Distribution Control Group
1. Health	4.0953	4.0119	.0834	1.038	1.1085
2. Physical Energy	4.25	4.1786	.0714	.9510	1.2470
3. Prudence and Forethought	4.5305	4.9405	.4100	1.174	.9570
4. Self-confidence	3.4165	4.1647	.7482	1.017	1.1095
5. Will-power, Perseverance	4.1190	4.4939	.3749	1.075	1.255
6. Musical Appreciation	4.3875	4.5743	.1868	.9285	.995
7. Appreciation of Beauty	4.0670	4.3441	.2771	.6320	.6810
8. Sense of Humor	4.1666	4.2143	.0477	1.2485	1.020
9. Cheerfulness, Optimism	3.7857	3.6403	.1454	1.207	1.027
10. Permanency of Moods	4.2256	4.0915	.1341	1.2925	1.2410
11. Fondness for Large Groups	3.7262	4.0595	.3333	1.069	1.175
12. Leadership	4.8215	4.5000	.3215	1.2325	1.1815
13. Popularity	4.2619	4.2622	.0003	.98495	.8590
14. Sensitiveness to Approval	3.6905	4.1125	.4220	1.24	1.14
15. Desire to Excel	4.1429	4.2143	.0714	1.1155	1.246
16. Freedom from Vanity and Egotism	4.2381	3.9286	.3095	1.1825	1.1225
17. Sympathy, Tenderness	3.3853	4.1191	.2738	1.0015	.8870
18. Generosity	3.9048	3.8875	.0173	1.003	.8875
19. Conscientiousness	4.0476	4.4573	.4097	1.0005	1.1840
20. Truthfulness	3.8691	3.9573	.0882	1.051	1.018
21. Mechanical Ingenuity	4.5263	4.4211	.1052	1.0495	.8215
22. Desire to Know	4.1548	4.3691	.2143	1.048	1.313
23. Originality	4.5595	4.9451	.3856	1.0575	1.131
24. Common Sense	4.1281	4.3453	.2172	.9290	1.1915
25. General Intelligence	4.4451	4.4762	.0311	1.244	1.0535

The next largest difference, and one having comparatively small variability, is that of sensitiveness to approval. Here the difference is equal to .4220 and the S.D. of this difference .2629, giving an experimental coefficient of .58, when 1. would indicate a real difference.

The number of judgments was comparatively small in this study (a consideration of significance in question of ratings). However, the data are at least suggestive of the marked similarity of stuttering and non-stuttering children on these ratings.

CHAPTER VI

PHYSICAL TRAITS

Physical examinations according to the program used in the Horace Mann School of Teachers College, Columbia University, were made by Miss Janet Shair and Mr. William J. Laub. [20: p. 201] On account of the difficulty in getting the children to come to the University, the number of subjects in this study was reduced to thirty-eight pairs, although eighty-four children were examined. Special attention was given the physical organs used in speaking.

1. *Breathing:*

MEASUREMENT	STUTTERERS	CONTROLS	DIFFERENCE
Lung Capacity			
Mean	112.0295 cu. in.	109.7840 cu. in.	2.2455 cu. in.
S.D.	32.195 cu. in.	28,985 cu. in.	
Chest Girth—Inspiration			
Mean	27.8158 in.	28.5 in.	.6842 in.
S.D.	2.617 in.	3.035 in.	
Chest Girth—Expiration			
Mean	25.7631 in.	25.6053 in.	.1578 in.
S.D.	2.602 in.	2.954 in.	
General Condition of Lungs			
"Normal"	100%	100%	

The S.D. of the difference between the two means of the distributions for lung capacity is 7.231. When this is divided into the difference we get .3 as an index of the reality of the difference. Real certainty would approximate 3.

Similar treatment of the larger difference between the means for chest girth, that for inspiration, gives a standard deviation of the difference of the means of .6504 and a ratio of the obtained difference (.6842) to this S.D. of the differences equal to 1.05, where 3 would approximate a certainty of difference between the groups. These data show no differences between the two groups in lung capacity or chest girth during inspiration or expiration.

The judgment of "normal" in the case of the condition of the lungs was arrived at by listening to the breathing with the purpose of detecting any unusual difficulties in the case of respiration. No cases of deviation from normal were found in either group.

2. *Hearing:*

The whisper and watch tests for hearing were given at the standard distances of 20, 30, and 40 feet between examiner and subject. All stutterers scored at normal 20/20; all but one of the controls at the same point, and this one exception was only slightly below normal, 20/18. Few deviations from normal were reported under "condition of ears"; "wax in the ears" was reported for 8 per cent of the stutterers and for 2.6 per cent of the controls. One stutterer had had a mastoid operation four years previously to the examination. One of the children in the control group had just been treated for an abscess in the right ear. Poor hearing is probably not a factor in the stuttering speech of the experimental group.

3. *Mouth, Tongue, and Teeth:*

CONDITION	PER CENT	
	Stutterers	Controls
Occlusion (closing of mouth—teeth)		
(1) Overbite		
(a) slight	33	45 +
(b) marked	15	26 —
(2) Approximation		
(a) "good"	30	19
(b) "fair"	15	26
(c) "poor"	33	35
Tongue		
(1) Tongue Tie		
(a) slight	9	10
(b) marked	12	3.2
(2) Coated	..	6
Teeth		
(1) General Condition		
(a) "excellent"	5	11
(b) "good"	8	6
(c) "fair"	..	2.9

CONDITION	PER CENT	
	Stutterers	Controls
Teeth (*Continued*)		
(2) Special Conditions		
(a) Stained	11	6
(b) Braces	5	2.9
(c) Ridged	..	2.9
(d) "Nicely cared for"	2.7	2.9
(e) Missing (does not include second and third permanent molars)	68	40
(f) Unfilled cavities	54	69
(g) Broken	2.7	
(h) Just erupting	14 —	14
(i) Erupting in front of another tooth.	2.7	..

Even here we have no substantial difference between the two groups. Inspection leads one to question whether the control group does not show more of a tendency to malocclusions of the mouth; but the ratio of the difference between the two proportions and the standard deviation of this difference is 1.8 per cent where 3.00 would indicate a real difference irrespective of chance variations.

4. *Throat and Nose:*

Examination of the noses and throats of the two groups gave no noticeable defects except that one stutterer was reported as having the "left nostril stuffed," and another stutterer as having a "deposit at the back of the throat." The uvula of one stutterer had been removed inadvertently during a tonsil operation. No attempt to inspect adenoids was made because of the discomfort

DEFECT	PER CENT	
	Stutterers	Controls
Tonsils		
Removed	61	50
Enlarged	34	34
Cryptic	2.6	..
Cervical Glands		
Swollen	34	32
Thyroid Glands		
Swollen	5	0

to the child sometimes involved in the examination. Tonsil, cervical gland, and thyroid gland inspection gave the information reported in the tabulation. No distinctive difference stands out from these results.

5. *Vision:*

The procedure recommended by Wood and Rowell was used in the examinations of vision. [20: p. 216] A study of the vision reports on the two groups revealed the following records on the Snellen charts:

| | PER CENT | |
CONDITION OF VISION	Stutterers	Controls
20/20 Normal		
Both eyes	61	55
Right eye only	28	16
Left eye only	8.3	5.2
20/30 Normal		
Both eyes	19	14
Right eye	8.3	5.2
Left eye	2.8	18
20/40 Normal		
Both eyes	...	...
Right eye	2.8	2.6
Left eye	...	2.6
20/50 Normal		
Both eyes	2.8	...
Right eye	...	2.6
Left eye	2.8	...
20/70 Normal		
Both eyes	2.8	...
Better than Normal, 20/15	...	2.6
Almost Normal, 20/25	...	2.6

Inspection of these differences indicates that they are so small that we cannot be sure they are real. When the two cases of vision approximately normal (one better, one slightly below) are combined with those having normal vision in both eyes, we get 23 cases out of 38, or 61 per cent, for the control group—exactly the proportion of stuttering children having normal vision or better.

Of the 36 stutterers, 17 showed symptoms of astigmatism in both eyes, 2 in the right eye only, and 1 in the left eye only.

The controls had 14 cases out of 38 having astigmatism in both eyes, 5 in the right eye only, and 2 in the left eye only. In each group 7 children were reported "slightly follicular; 1 in each as having pale eyes," and 2 stutterers as having marked circles under the eyes. One stutterer was inadvertently omitted from the eye examinations. The record of another was unintelligible to the writer, hence the disparity in numbers between the two groups.

Information about the conditions of vision among stutterers is especially interesting because of a popular notion that left-handedness is connected with superiority of vision in the left eye, and that left-handedness is closely connected with stuttering. These data give no indication that stutterers are different from the children of the control group in accuracy of vision.

6. *Strength of Grip in Right and in Left Hand:*

An examination of the results of the tests for the strength of grip in each hand may be interesting here because of its having been associated with vision in popular notions:

STRENGTH OF GROUP	POUNDS PRESSURE		
	Stutterers	Controls	Difference
Right Hand			
Mean	39.341	39.6055	.2645
S.D.	13.25	12.49	
Left Hand			
Mean	37.6315	37.3685	.2630
S.D.	14.515	12.15	
Equal strength in both hands	16—per cent	24—per cent	
Right stronger than left	61—per cent	63—per cent	
Left stronger than right	24—per cent	14—per cent	

In the case of the largest difference, that of 10 per cent more stutterers having more strength in the left hand, the percentages were treated statistically in order to determine the reality of the difference:

Difference was 10 per cent.
S.D. of difference, .0567.
Experimental coefficient .63, where 1. would indicate certainty of a real difference.

Ballard found that stuttering was more frequent among left-handed children than among right-handed, and that it was exceptionally prevalent among left-handed children who had been taught to write with the right hand. He says one in every six stammerers [stutterers] is left-handed. [21: p. 309] Terman accepts Ballard's investigation as having "established the point beyond controversy." [22: p. 345] Wallin's study did not bear out Ballard's claims. [12: p. 215] Out of a total of 89,057 school children, 1.844 were reported as "dextro-sinistrals" (or left-handed children taught to use the right hand); however, only 9.4 per cent had acquired any speech defects, although all had been taught to write with the right hand, and many of those having speech difficulties had acquired them before they had been taught to write at all.

The existence of "dextro-sinistrality" was determined in Ballard's study by a questionnaire and no definite limitations were set upon the meaning of the word. The children testified that they were once "left-handed, and later had been taught to write with the right hand."

It is doubtful whether in this study strength of grip may be taken as a measure of handedness but in the event that such interpretation of muscular control is justifiable, we have no indication of a difference between these groups.

7. *Posture:*

Each child was rated on a scale of five places for posture: 5 meant satisfactory, good; 4, fair; 3, poor; 2, very poor; and 1, marked deformity.

The two groups appeared about equal in posture ratings:

RATING	PER CENT	
	Stutterers	Controls
5 (satisfactory)	2.9	5
4 (fair)	31	26
3 (poor)	51	50
2 (very poor)	14	18
1 (marked deformity)		

A detailed analysis of the specific deviations from normal posture gave the data reported in the tabulation on the following page. Apparently poor posture cannot be said to be a distinctive trait of this group of stutterers if we take these data into consideration.

DEVIATION FROM NORMAL	PER CENT	
	Stutterers	Controls
Shoulders		
Round	34	29
Winged scapula	47	53
Left shoulder higher than right	16—	21
Right shoulder higher than left	18	11
Drooping shoulders	..	5
Abdomen		
Prominent, protruding	71	58
Pelvis tilted	2.6	..
Spine		
Hollow back	5	..
Sway back	..	2.6
Right thoracic curve	2.6	..
Slight left general curve	2.6	..
Left lumbar curve	2.6	..
Right lumbar curve	..	2.6
Chest		
Flat chest	..	5
Feet		
Pronation marked	58	66
Club foot	5	8
Muscular injury	2.6	2.6

8. *General Health*

In addition to the organs of breathing, articulation, hearing, and the like, the "general" health of the children was taken into consideration. Each of the examiners gave a judgment on the apparent general health conditions and nervous state of the subject. These ratings gave the following percentages:

GENERAL HEALTH	PER CENT	
	Stutterers	Controls
"Good"	89	87
"Fair"	11	13
"Poor"	0	0

9. *Nervousness*

Following are judgments about the apparent "nervousness" of the children during examination:

Stutterers .... 29 per cent
Controls .... 26 per cent

10. *Condition of Skin* (Cleanliness, etc.):

CONDITION OF SKIN	PER CENT	
	Stutterers	Controls
"Good"	100	92
"Poor"	...	2.6
"Fair"	...	...
"Rough" on arms and face	...	5.4

These examiners were unacquainted with the subjects and did not know which belonged to the experimental and which to the control group. Evidently the members of the experimental group presented no obvious difficulties in general health, "nervousness," or skin conditions which would distinguish them from children who do not stutter.

11. *Weight, Height, and Nutrition-Weight:*

A comparison of the weight of the two groups yielded these facts:

WEIGHT	STUTTERERS	CONTROLS
Mean	72.158	69.4735
S.D.	20.905	18.265

The difference between means was 3.6845, a very small one in comparison to the size of the standard deviations.

The standard deviation of the means was 4.503, making the ratio between the difference and the S.D. of the difference .9, when 3.0 would indicate a real difference beyond the limits of chance variation.

Similar conclusions may be drawn from the data on height.

In the reports on "nutrition-weight" (weight compared with the average for his height), we find the same agreement between the records for the two groups which were equivalent in chronological and mental age and racial inheritance.

HEIGHT	STUTTERERS	CONTROLS
Mean	54.1842	53.8158
S.D.	4.572	4.719
Difference between means	.3684	......
S.D. of the differences	1.006	......
Ratio	.34	......

NUTRITION-WEIGHT	Stutterers	Controls
Below average	63%	63%
Mean of deviations from average	4.9	6.2
Above average	37%	37%
Mean of deviations from normal	9.9	8.0

12. *Heart Rate and Blood Pressure:*

	STUTTERERS	CONTROLS	DIFFERENCE
Heart Rate			
Mean	102.763	99.4735	3.2895
S.D.	15.215	15.07	
Blood Pressure			
(1) Systolic			
Mean	95.076	93.409	1.667
S.D.	12.62	10.40	
(2) Diastolic			
Mean	63.106	65.076	1.970
S.D.	12.045	8.80	

In no case does the difference between the means become large enough in comparison with the S.D. to warrant the assumption of a real difference.

A more definite description of the heart conditions in the two groups is shown in the tabulation which is given on the opposite page.

Generally speaking, none of the data gathered from physical examinations of the members of both the experimental and control groups show an appreciable difference between the two groups when one takes into consideration the operation of chance factors in the testing conditions. These data, however, do not adequately represent many subtle physical differences which may exist; metabolism and glandular secretion are notable examples of this fact.

CONDITION	PER CENT	
	Stutterers	Controls
Normal	89	87
(Normal but rapid)	(2.6)	(5)
Slight mitral thrill	5	5
Marked mitral thrill	2.6	
Mitral stenosis, heart rate irregular, harsh		5
Skipped beat (irregular)	2.6	2.6

CHAPTER VII

SPEECH DIFFICULTIES OTHER THAN STUTTERING

Tests for pronunciation of the various sounds of English speech and offering the subject three opportunities to make each sound according to his habitual use of it were devised by the experimenter. The sounds were:

1. Vowels: *ah* (*father*), *a* (*ate*), *e* (*eat*), *aw* (*awe*), *oh* (*obey*), *u* (*cruel*), *a* (*Dan*), *e* (*pen*), *i* (*milk*), *o* (*hot*), *u* (*sun*).
2. Diphthongs: *iu* (*you*), *oi* (*boil*), *au* (*out*), *ai* (*fire*), *er* (*burn*).
3. Consonants: *p, b, m, w, wh, f, v, th* (voiced), *th* (breathed), *t, d, n, l, r, s, z, sh, zh, k, g, ng* (the single sound), *h*.
4. Combinations:
   (1) Initial *pl, bl, br, pr.*
       Final *pt, bd, md, ps, bg, mz.*
   (2) Initial *fl, fr.*
       Final *ft, vd, vn, fs, vz.*
   (3) Initial *thr.*
       Final *ths, thd, thz.*
   (4) Initial *tr, dr, tw, tsh, dzh.*
       Final *nth, dth, nt, nd, tn, dn, ts, ns, dz, tl, ol, nz, tsh, dzh.*
   (5) Final *lz, lp, lm, lf, lv, lth, lt, ls, ld, lk.*
   (6) Initial *sw, st, sm, sn, sl, str, skr, sk, shr, skw, sp.*
       Final *st, sp, sn, sts, zd, zl, sl, sk, zm, sht.*
   (7) Initial *kr, gr, gl, kl, kw.*
       Final *gl, kl, kn, ks, gz, gd.*
   (8) Final *(ng)d, (ng)z, (ng)k.*
   (9) Miscellaneous combinations—*fths, ksths, pths, kts.*

The sentences containing the sounds listed above in groups **1**, **2**, and **3** were read to the individual, who repeated them after

34

the examiner. They were broken up into phrases corresponding to the natural grouping of the meaning of the sentence so that efforts to remember the words would not greatly interfere with the repetition. Each consonant occurred three times in all three of its initial, middle, and final positions. The subject was asked to "say these sentences after me just the way I say them."

The sounds omitted or substituted were recorded on the test blank and subsequently summarized for each individual, and later for each group. Comparisons were made on the basis of the percentages of subjects in each group mispronouncing the sound.

A study of voice and phonation difficulties probably would have been more to the point than those of articulation, because of the stutterer's inability to produce voice, but it was thought to be impracticable here because of the subjective nature of all measures of voice inadequacy.

Results of the tests for articulation difficulties are summarized thus:

SPEECH DIFFICULTY	NUMBER OF STUTTERERS	NUMBER OF CONTROLS
1. Vowels		
ah—substitution of *e* (as in *eat*)	1	..
substitution of *aw* (as in *awe*)	1	..
e—substitution of *e* (as in *pet*)	1	..
substitution of *i* (as in *pie*)	..	2
oh—substitution of *oi* (as in *boil*)	..	2
substitution of *er* (as in *pert*)	1	..
substitution of *i* (as in *bite*)	1	..
substitution of *ao* (as in *house*)	1	..
oo—substitution of *i*	1	1
a (short)—substitution of *i*	2	..
nasalized	..	2
o (short)—substitution of *a* (as in *hat*)	..	1
Total	9	8
2. Diphthongs		
iu—substitution of *oo* (as in *boot*)	6	9
oi—substitution of *er* (as in *pert*)	8	10
substitution of *aw* (as in *awe*)	1	..
ou—substitution of *oo* (as in *boot*)	1	..
substitution of *oi* (as in *boil*)	1	1
substitution of *a* (as in *father*)	..	1
substitution of *a* (as in *hat*)	..	1

Speech Difficulty	Number of Stutterers	Number of Controls
2. Diphthongs (*Continued*)		
au—substitution of *au* (as in *hat*)	3	..
substitution of *oo* (as in *boot*)	1	..
er—substitution of *oi* (as in *boil*)	3	..
substitution of *oo* (as in *boot*)	2	2
Total	26	24
3. Single Consonants		
p—omission (middle position in word) ...	3	2
omission (final position in word)	4	2
substitution of *t* (final)	..	1
b—omission (middle)	1	1
omission (final)	1	4
substitution of *d* (middle)	1	..
substitution of *v* (final)	6	5
m—omission (middle)	1	1
omission (final)	1	..
substitution of *n*	..	1
w—omission (middle)	1	..
wh—substitution of *w* (initial)	25	25
substitution of *w* (middle)	14	10
f—omission (final)	..	1
substitution of *th* (final)	1	..
substitution of *m* (final)	..	1
v—omission (initial)	1	2
substitution of *f* (initial)	1	3
substitution of *f* (final)	8	11
substitution of *w* (initial)	1	2
substitution of *b* (initial)	1	..
substitution of *th* (final)	..	1
th (breathed)—omission (final)	..	3
substitution of *f* (initial).	2	1
substitution of *f* (middle)	2	1
substitution of *f* (final) ..	1	2
substitution of *t* (initial).	2	4
substitution of *t* (middle)	5	..
substitution of *t* (final) ..	9	2
substitution of *th* (voiced) (final)	1	2
th (voiced)—substitution of *d* (initial) ...	1	..
substitution of *d* (middle)..	2	2
substitution of *d* (final)	2	1
substitution of *t* (initial) ..	..	1
substitution of *t* (middle) ..	2	..
substitution of *t* (final)	1	1

SPEECH DIFFICULTY	NUMBER OF STUTTERERS	NUMBER OF CONTROLS
3. Single Consonants (*Continued*)		
th (voiced)—substitution of *v* (middle)..	4	3
substitution of *v* (final)	4	1
substitution of *f* (middle) ..	1	..
substitution of *f* (final)	1	..
substitution of *th* (breathed) (middle)	2	..
substitution of *th* (breathed) (final)	1	4
substitution of *d* (middle)..	2	2
substitution of *d* (final)	2	1
addition of *s* (middle)	1	..
t—omission (middle)	5	3
omission (final)	4	5
d—omission (middle)	1	1
omission (final)	1	1
substitution of *g* (initial)	1	..
substitution of *t* (middle)	..	1
substitution of *t* (final)	1	..
n—omission (final)	1	1
l—omission (final)	..	1
substitution of *r* (initial)	1	..
substitution of *w* (middle)	2	..
substitution of *f* (middle)	1	..
r—omission (middle)	4	2
substitution of *w* (middle)	2	3
substitution of *l* (middle)	2	..
s—side lisp	6	6
hiss	3	6
substitution of *sh* (initial)	1	..
substitution of *th* (final)	1	..
sh—substitution of *j* (initial)	1	..
zh—substitution of *j* (initial)	2	..
substitution of *j* (middle)	1	..
substitution of *j* (final)	5	4
substitution of *z* (middle)	2	..
substitution of *sh* (final)	1	6
substitution of *sh* (middle)	..	1
substitution of *ch* (final)	..	2
k—omission (middle)	..	1
substitution of *g* (middle)	1	..
g—omission (final)	..	2
substitution of *d* (initial)	1	..
substitution of *d* (final)	..	1
(*ng*)—addition of *g* (middle)	6	2

Speech Difficulty	Number of Stutterers	Number of Controls
3. Single Consonants (*Continued*)		
(*ng*)—addition of *g* (final)	4	7
omission (final)	2	..
h—omission (initial)	2	1
omission (middle)	3	1
substitution of *g* (initial)	1	..
substitution of *b* (initial)	..	1
substitution of *b* (middle)	1	..
z—substitution of *s* (initial)	2	3
substitution of *s* (middle)	3	2
substitution of *s* (final)	2	1
substitution of *d* (middle)	1	..
substitution of *er* (middle)	..	1
substitution of *ag* (middle)	..	1
4. Combinations		
Initial		
pl—omission of *l*	1	..
pr—omission of *r*	2	1
substitution of *w*	3	1
br—omission of *r*	1	..
substitution of *w*	2	..
fl—omission of *l*	1	..
fr—omission of *r*	3	..
substitution of *w*	3	..
substitution of *l*	1	..
thr—substitution of *t*	2	2
substitution of *tw*	1	..
substitution of *f*	1	1
substitution of *ch*	..	1
tr—substitution of *tw*	1	..
dr—substitution of *dw*	1	..
substitution of *tr*	1	..
sw—substitution of *sp*	1	..
st—substitution of *sth*	2	..
substitution of *t*	1	..
substitution of *sh*	1	..
sp—substitution of *sk*	1	1
sn—substitution of *sm*	..	1
str—substitution of *shr*	1	..
substitution of *stw*	..	1
shr—substitution of *sr*	2	2
substitution of *thr*	..	1
substitution of *sw*	1	..
omission of *r*	1	..

Speech Difficulty	Number of Stutterers	Number of Controls
4. Combinations (*Continued*)		
Initial (*Continued*)		
shr—substitution of slr	1	..
sk—substitution of th	1	..
omissions of k	1	..
kr—omissions of r	1	1
substitution of kw	2	1
substitution of tr	1	..
Final		
pt—omission of t	1	1
bd—omission of d	3	6
omission of bd	1	..
substitution of bt	14	11
substitution of g	1	..
md—omission of d	3	5
substitution of nd	2	1
substitution of nt	1	..
substitution of mt	12	12
bz—substitution of bs	13	17
mz—substitution of ms	11	16
omission of z	1	..
ft—omission of t	2	1
addition of s	1	..
vd—substitution of vt	11	13
substitution of ft	1	..
substitution of f	..	1
substitution of vz	1	..
omission of d	2	3
omission of v	1	..
vn—addition of t	1	..
substitution of fn	..	1
fs—substitution of ps	3	..
substitution of vs	..	1
substitution of p	1	..
omission of s	1	2
addition of t	2	..
vz—substitution of vs	10	16
substitution of fs	2	2
substitution of bs	1	..
substitution of fz	..	2
substitution of ts	..	1
omission of v	1	..
ths—omission of th	4	1
omission of s	5	3
substitution of ts	5	3

Speech Difficulty	Number of Stutterers	Number of Controls
4. Combinations (*Continued*)		
Final (*Continued*)		
ths—substitution of *st*	2	1
substitution of *thz*	..	1
substitution of *fs*	2	2
substitution of *fts*	1	..
substitution of *ps*	2	..
substitution of *ds*	1	..
substitution of *vs*	1	..
thd—substitution of *t*	11	16
substitution of *ts*	1	..
substitution of *vd*	3	..
substitution of *ft*	1	..
omission of *th*	4	1
omission of *d*	8	6
substitution of *td*	..	1
thz—omission of *th*	9	10
substitution of *th* (breathed)	3	1
substitution of *ts*	6	3
substitution of *vs*	1	..
substitution of *vz*	2	2
substitution of *ds*	2	..
substitution of *d*	1	..
substitution of *tds*	1	..
nth—substitution of *nt*	3	3
substitution of *nd*	1	..
substitution of *f*	1	..
omission of *th*	3	1
dth—omission of *d*	10	13
omission of *th*	3	3
substitution of *t*	3	2
substitution of *v*	1	..
substitution of *vd*	1	..
substitution of *dt*	1	..
substitution of *tth*	..	1
substitution of *ts*	..	2
addition of *s*	1	..
addition of *ick*	1	..
nt—omission of *n*	2	2
nd—omission of *d*	3	3
substitution of *nt*	2	5
substitution of *nth*	..	1
tn—substitution of *dn*	1	..
dn—substitution of *tn*	..	2
substitution of *dun*	1	..

·

Speech Difficulty	Number of Stutterers	Number of Controls
4. Combinations (*Continued*)		
Final (*Continued*)		
dn—omission of *d*	1	..
ts—omission of *s*	1	..
dz—substitution of *ds*	12	15
substitution of *ch*	1	..
substitution of *j*	..	1
omission of *z*	1	..
tl—omission of *t*	1	..
substitution of *d*	1	..
dl—substitution of *tl*	2	..
substitution of *vld*	1	..
nz—substitution of *ns*	12	12
dzh(j)—substitution of *ch*	5	3
substitution of *dch*	..	1
substitution of *sh*	..	1
lz—substitution of *ls*	14	15
lp—substitution of *lt*	1	1
omission of *l*	3	..
omission of *lp*	1	..
substitution of *lf*	1	..
lm—substitution of *em*	..	1
substitution of *um*	..	1
omission of *l*	..	1
omission of *m*	1	..
addition of *s*	1	..
lf—substitution of *v*	1	..
substitution of *t*	..	1
lv—substitution of *lf*	8	12
substitution of *lp*	1	..
omission of *l*	1	1
lth—substitution of *lt*	3	2
substitution of *fth*	2	1
substitution of *lf*	..	..
lt—substitution of *d*	..	1
omission of *t*	1	1
ls—omission of *l*	2	..
substitution of *lst*	1	..
ld—substitution of *lt*	9	9
omission of *d*	4	1
lk—substitution of *lt*	1	..
st—omission of *t*	2	2
substitution of *kst*	1	..
substitution of *k*	..	1
substitution of *sh*	1	..

Speech Difficulty	Number of Stutterers	Number of Controls
4. Combinations (*Continued*)		
Final (*Continued*)		
sp—substitution of *ps*	6	1
substitution of *pst*	2	1
substitution of *st*	2	1
substitution of *fts*	1	..
substitution of *sk*	1	..
substitution of *sm*	1	..
omission of *p*	2	1
addition of *t*	1	..
sn—substitution of *shn*	1	..
sts—omission of *s*	10	12
omission of *t*	6	2
omission of *st*	4	..
substitution of *kst*	1	..
substitution of *k*	1	1
substitution of *sk*	..	1
substitution of *ps*	..	1
zn—substitution of *sn*	..	1
zd—substitution of *zt*	12	12
omission of *d*	4	4
sl—substitution of *d*	1	..
sk—substitution of *st*	2	3
omission of *k*	..	2
omission of *t*	..	1
zm—substitution of *zn*	1	1
substitution of *mum*	1	..
omission of *zm*	1	..
sht—omission of *t*	3	..
substitution of *zd*	1	..
substitution of *ksth*	1	..
shd—substitution of *sht*	..	1
omission of *d*	..	1
zl—substitution of *sl*	1	1
gl—omission of *g*	..	1
substitution of *ll*	..	1
substitution of *t*	..	1
kl—substitution of *ll*	..	1
kt—substitution of *kd*	..	1
omission of *k*	4	..
omission of *t*	2	1
kn—omission of *n*	..	1
substitution of *tn*	..	1
ks—omission of *k*	1	..
gz—omission of *g*	1	..

Speech Difficulty	Number of Stutterers	Number of Controls
4. Combinations (*Continued*)		
Final (*Continued*)		
gz—substitution of *gs*	9	11
substitution of *dz*	..	1
ngd—substitution of *ngt*	9	7
omission of *d*	4	3
addition of *g*	..	1
ngz—substitution of *ngs*	10	5
omission of *g*	1	..
ngk—substitution of *t*	2	..
fths—omission of *f*	2	3
omission of *th*	5	8
omission of *s*	2	1
substitution of *ft*	1	1
substitution of *t*	1	1
substitution of *fts*	1	2
substitution of *ts*	..	1
ksths—omission of *th*	5	8
omission of *ths*	2	2
omission of *s*	2	4
substitution of *ksts*	2	1
substitution of *kst*	4	3
substitution of *ksk*	1	..
substitution of *tist*	1	..
pths—substitution of *fs*	3	..
omission of *p*	2	3
omission of *th*	7	10
substitution of *pts*	2	..
substitution of *fs*	1	..
substitution of *ts*	1	4
substitution of *dith*	1	..
omission of *s*	..	3
omission of *pth*	..	1
kts—omission of *t*	10	20
omission of *k*	7	2
omission of *kt*	1	..
substitution of *st*	1	1
substitution of *th*	1	..
gd—substitution of *t*	10	6
substitution of *z*	1	..
substitution of *gk*	..	1
omission of *d*	2	2
Total	380	333

SUMMARY TABLE FOR ALL SPEECH SOUNDS

	STUTTERERS	CONTROLS
1. Vowels		
Total number of subjects mispronouncing..	9	8
Chances for error (33 x 11)	363	363
	(2.5%)	(2.2%)
2. Diphthongs		
Total number of subjects mispronouncing..	26	24
Chances for errors (33 x 5)	165	165
	(16%)	(14.5%)
3. Single Consonants		
Total number of subjects mispronouncing..	197	171
Chances for errors (33 x 22)	726	726
	(27%)	(24%)
4. Initial Combinations		
Total number of subjects mispronouncing..	169	137
Chances for error (33 x 28)	924	924
	(18%)	(15%)
5. Final Combinations		
Total number of subjects mispronouncing..	380	333
Chances for error (33 x 61)	2013	2013
	(18%)	(17%)

(Multiplicand = number of subjects, 33; multiplier = number of sounds presented for testing.)

In the case of the largest difference and the greatest number of chances for error (initial combinations) the results were treated statistically for the possibility of finding a real difference. The standard deviation for the difference between the two proportions was .0173; the difference .03, and the experimental coefficient .6 certainty. Again we fail to find a marked disparity between the groups.

However, if we consider the total number of incorrect responses for each group, we do have indications of a real difference between them.

	STUTTERERS	CONTROLS
Total number of errors made	781	673
Total chances for errors made	4,191	4,191
Per cent of errors made	19%	16%

S.D. of difference between per cents of each group .... .00829
Experimental coefficient.. 1.3

The value of these data is very questionable because of certain varying factors in the testing situation brought on by the subjective nature of the scoring. The tests were made by three different persons, all of whom had been trained in accurate recognition of speech sounds; however, the judgments in accuracy of ear are necessarily subjective. Each judge should have been "standardized" in her discrimination of sounds by some such process as that used in tests for the training of scorers on handwriting scales, or on the merits of composition, etc. At any rate the data may be suggestive for further investigations into the speech difficulties of stutterers.

CHAPTER VIII

CONCLUSIONS AND SUMMARY

The data which have been assembled may be disappointing to those wishing more positive conclusions concerning the relationship between stuttering and nervous disorder. The angles from which we have been able to study the two groups have shown a surprising amount of similarity between the stutterers and the controls. It is impossible to say how much this similarity was predetermined by our method of selection. Both kinds of tests—those administered to investigate parallelism in physical and mental characteristics and those used in choosing groups equivalent in certain traits—may have tended to select children parallel in characteristics which we did not seek to parallel. Emotional attitudes are an important consideration in getting a valid measure of intelligence on the Binet test, for example, and some failure to establish a situation in which tester and subject were *en rapport* may have tended to select a control group not equivalent to the experimental group in the trait (intelligence) in which we wished them to be equivalent.

One of the devices for comparing the emotional and personality traits has decided limitations in the fact that the subjective element could not be eliminated. Teachers who made the ratings on the trait scales were acquainted with the subjects and knew which of them stuttered. Many teachers, also, were familiar with the popular notion that stutterers are thought to be unusually timid and sensitive to social approval and they may have been influenced by that knowledge in rating stutterers on these counts.

The true value of the tests used to compare mental and emotional traits is, of course, subject to question. However, in a quantitative study of a characteristic as elusive as temperament and personality we may feel we have made some progress if we have come upon even suggestions of probable facts concerning conditions to be submitted to further investigation. The tests used were selected because they offered the nearest approach to a reliable measure of the traits and capacities to be investigated which careful workmanship has yet devised. We cannot be sure that the Woodworth-Cady and Woodworth-Matthews questionnaires offer a valid judgment of persons having psychotic tendencies, yet we cannot be sure they do not do so, in view of their high correlation with commonly accepted marks of inadequate social and emotional adapations. The chances perhaps are in favor of their doing so. Such is the case with other tests used in the studies.

If the conditions pointed to by these findings should be accepted as true, the procedure for corrective work with stuttering individuals would naturally swing toward a marked emphasis on the improvement of speech habits rather than upon the eradication of neuropathic or psychopathic tendencies in the individual. A valuable procedure for checking the findings of this investigation would be a comparative study of groups of stutterers, equivalent in mental maturity and capacity as well as in past opportunity for acquiring good speech, each of which could be treated in rotation with one technique designed to improve speech habits, another to eliminate psychopathic conditions, and a third to improve the neuropathic or physical disabilities which might be present in the individuals.

SUMMARY

A résumé and summary tables of the results of the comparisons of stutterers with non-stutterers may be helpful in evaluating the data which form the basis of these studies.

1. Stuttering, when defined as hesitant speech accompanied by spasms of the muscles of the throat and diaphragm and showing special inability to produce voiced sounds, was found to be present in .9 per cent of the population of seven schools enrolling 7,138 children, in a degree marked enough to be reported by the teachers. This proportion is similar to the findings of Wallin, Conradi, and the majority of investigators upon this subject in the United States and Europe.

2. The intelligence quotients of this group on the Stanford Revision of the Binet Intelligence Test ranged from 64 to 156 with a mean of 99.14 and a standard deviation of 20.38. The subjects came from schools having very different types of patrons and probably representing a fair sampling of the public and

private schools of New York City. At any rate they represent a "normal" group when measured by the standards established for the test.

3. When compared to a control group equated on the basis of chronological age, mental age, sex, racial inheritance, and language background, their performance on the Pintner-Patterson Non-Language Intelligence Test is better than that of the controls by 4.4 points. The variation of the two groups is so large that the standard deviation of this difference, 4.988, makes it insignificant, as it might easily have arisen from chance variation in the selection of subjects, only .3 of certainty.

4. When the tests most obviously dependent upon language abilities were selected from the Binet tests, and comparisons between the two groups made, the difference between them on the Free Association Test was only .5555 in favor of the controls, with a standard deviation of this difference equal to 5.032 and an experimental coefficient of only .04 certainty. This test required the subject to say as many words as he could within a three-minute time limit. In spite of the stutterer's speech handicap he seems to have done as well as the non-stuttering child.

In the Vocabulary Test asking for the meanings of words, the difference between these two groups was only .6935 in favor of the stuttering children with a standard deviation of this difference equal to 2.58, and an experimental coefficient of .097 certainty. Consequently, we judge that whatever be the differences between stuttering and non-stuttering children, these differences are probably not concerned with special language aptitudes.

5. In school achievement we find no significant disparity between the two groups. The accomplishment quotients measured by the Stanford Achievement Tests for reading, arithmetic, and spelling showed a superiority of the controls equal to 3.068 points, but the standard deviation of the difference was 2.703, making the experimental coefficient only .408 certainty that this difference is real. An analysis of the various tests included in the Stanford Achievement collection showed in every case a slight superiority of the control group, but the differences became insignificant when their reliability was investigated. The test most nearly approaching certainty of a real difference was that in arithmetic (computation), where the experimental coefficient was only .25

of certainty. These data challenge the claims of many writers who maintain that stuttering is a direct cause of retardation in school subjects.

6. In emotional readjustments as · measured by the Woodworth-Cady, Woodworth-Matthews Questionnaires, the Kent-Rosanoff Association Tests, and teachers' judgments, we find the groups to be very similar. On the two questionnaires, responses indicating "psychotic tendencies" were more numerous in the case of stutterers by 2.52 points; however, variability in the two groups was so great that the standard deviation of this difference was 2.04 and the experimental coefficient only .44 of certainty. Analysis of the individual questions showed no significant differences between the percentage of stutterers answering unfavorably and the percentage of the controls, except in the case of "Do you get out of breath very quickly when you run?" The difference here was 2.4 per cent and the experimental coefficient .907. Other questions most nearly approximating a real difference were: "Does it make you uneasy to cross a bridge over water?" (experimental coefficient .75 certainty); "Do you talk in your sleep?" (experimental coefficient .75 certainty); and "Do you have a hard time making up your mind about things?" (experimental coefficient .74 certainty).

In the Kent-Rosanoff Association Test we find no significant difference between the stutterers and the controls either in reaction times or in the quality of the responses. The difference between the mid-scores of the reaction times was .2 seconds (experimental coefficient .31); that between the point of location for the upper quartiles, .5463 seconds (experimental coefficient .455). The percentage of "excessive" reaction times, those lying far beyond the normal distribution of the individual's responses (8 seconds or more), did show evidence of a real difference between the groups. Nine per cent of the reactions of the stutterers and 7 per cent of those of the controls lay beyond this point. The standard deviation of the difference (2 per cent) was equal to .005466, giving an experimental coefficient of 1.3 where 1. would be certainty of a real difference. None of the words having the prolonged reaction time was particularly diagnostic, however, in any of the cases where the percentage of prolonged response was large enough to be treated statistically for the reliability of their differences.

The quality of the responses in the two groups showed no appreciable differences. In common reactions the difference in favor of the controls was 1.2195, with a standard deviation of 4.8096, giving an experimental coefficient of only .09 certainty. Individual responses showed a difference of .3655 (S.D. 4.6588) for stutterers, and an experimental coefficient of only .028 certainty. "Doubtful" responses of stutterers had a mean .9756 points higher than that for controls, but the standard deviation of the difference was .8586, giving an experimental coefficient of only .409 certainty.

"Key" words suggestive of ideas reputed to have special emotional significance for stutterers were no more useful in showing a difference between the groups than was the standard word list. Mid-scores of the reaction times on these words gave a difference of .08 seconds in favor of the stutterers, with a standard deviation of .2424, and an experimental coefficient of .12. The location of the upper quartile point was .62 seconds higher for the stutterers than for the controls, but the standard deviation of this difference was .5498, giving an experimental coefficient of .4 certainty.

Qualitative responses to "key" words also failed to show a difference between stutterers, for 46 per cent of both groups gave common reactions; 44 per cent of stutterers and 46 per cent of controls gave individual reactions; and 9.8 per cent of stutterers and 8 per cent of controls gave doubtful reactions. In no case were experimental coefficients significant (individual reactions .3, and doubtful .5).

Teachers' ratings of the two groups of twenty-five traits of character and personality showed marked similarity between the two groups on every point except that of self-confidence where the experimental coefficient of 1.15 indicated the superiority of the control group in the opinion of the teachers.

6. In physical traits marked similarity of the two groups was evident. The difference in weight was 3.6845 in favor of stutterers and the experimental coefficient .3 certainty. In height the difference was .3684 inches in favor of stutterers with an experimental coefficient of .12 certainty. "Nutrition-weight" scores (weight of the child compared with average for his height) showed 63 per cent of the children of each group to be below average, with the average of the deviations at 4.9 pounds for

stutterers and 6.1 pounds for controls. The mean of the deviations of the 37 per cent of stutterers testing above average was 9.9 pounds, that of the same proportion of controls, 8.0 pounds.

Stutterers had a heart rate of 3.2895 points faster than that of controls but again variability in the groups was so great that the experimental coefficient was only .34 certainty. The general condition of the heart was reported "normal" in 89 per cent of stutterers and in 87 per cent of the controls. Such irregularities as mitral stenosis, murmurs, and the like were about evenly divided between the remaining proportion of the two groups. Blood pressure in the systolic phase of the cycle was 1.667 points higher among stutterers than among controls (experimental coefficient .21); while in the diastolic phase the difference was 1.532 points higher for the controls, giving slightly more variability in the cycle on the part of stutterers.

"General condition" was reported "good" in 89 per cent of the stutterers and in 87 per cent of the controls. The remaining children of both groups were said to be in "fair" condition. The skin was reported in "good" condition in 100 per cent of the cases of the stutterers and in 92 per cent of the controls. Ratings of posture were almost identical, no particular element standing out in either group. Twenty-nine per cent of the stutterers and 26 per cent of the controls exhibited symptoms of "nervousness" during the examinations.

In physical traits thought to be more intimately connected with the acquisition of speech skills we find similar lack of marked difference between the two groups. Lung capacity was slightly higher for stutterers, a difference of 2.432 cubic inches (experimental coefficient .12). Chest girth during inspiration was .3158 inches greater for stutterers (experimental coefficient .18); at expiration .1578 cubic inches greater for the same group. Strength of grip in the right arm was higher for controls by .2635 pounds pressure (experimental coefficient .03); and in the left arm .2630 pounds pressure higher for stutterers (experimental coefficient .03). These data cannot be interpreted as indicative of a tendency to left-handedness in stutterers because of the great variability in the performance of the individuals as shown by the size of the experimental coefficients. The proportion of subjects showing greater strength in the left hand was 24 per cent among stutterers and 14 per cent among controls. The standard deviation of the difference between these proportions was .0893, giving an experimental coefficient of .4. Vision, which is some- times thought to be connected with handedness, was about nor- mal in 61 per cent of the children of each group. Astigmatism was present in both groups in about the same proportion. Hear- ing was uniformly "normal." No distinctive differences were found in the conditions of the nose and throat or in the articula- tion of the teeth which could account for stuttering. There was a report of "missing" teeth 28 per cent higher in stutterers than controls, but this was a temporary condition and is accounted for by the fact that many children were acquiring their second teeth.

8. In the total number of errors in speech pronunciation we do find a difference in favor of the accuracy of the controls (ex- perimental coefficient 1.3) ; however in no one of the single groups of kinds of speech sounds do we find a difference large enough to be diagnostic.

SUMMARY TABLE OF DIFFERENCES IN TEST RESULTS FOR STUTTERERS AND CONTROL GROUP

TEST	MEAN OF STUTTERERS	MEAN OF CONTROL GROUP	S.D. OF DISTRIBUTION OF STUTTERERS	S.D. OF DISTRIBUTION OF CONTROLS	S.D. OF MEAN OF STUTTERERS	S.D. OF MEAN OF CONTROLS	S.D. OF DIFF. OF MEANS	DIFFERENCE OBTAINED	RATIO OF DIFF. TO S.D. OF DIFF. OF MEANS	EXPERIMENTAL COEFFICIENT
I. Intelligence Tests Binet—for all Stutterers (61 subjects) I.Q.	99.14		20.380							
II. Pintner-Patterson Non-Language Intelligence Tests A. Equating Groups 1. Binet, M.A.	122.6	123.2	25.5830	26.344				.6		
2. Binet, I.Q.	101.9	102.0	19.866	20.255				.1		
B. Test Results 1. Pintner-Patterson, I.Q.	104.20	99.8	26.732	23.005	3.7805	3.2534	4.988	In favor of Exp. Group 4.4	.88126	.317
2. Binet Free Association Test	61.1665	69.7220	26.771	20.563	3.9908	3.0654	5.032	In favor of Control Group .5555	.1112	.040
3. Binet Vocabulary Test (50 prs. subjects)	31.2448	30.551	12.078	13.427	1.7254	1.9181	2.5799	Experimental .6938	.26966	.097

Test	Mean of Stutterers	Mean of Control Group	S.D. of Distribution of Stutterers	S.D. of Distribution of Controls	S.D. of Mean of Stutterers	S.D. of Mean of Controls	S.D. of Diff. of Means	Difference Obtained	Ratio of Diff. to S.D. of Diff. of Means	Experimental Coefficient
III. Stanford Achievement Tests										
A. Equating Groups										
1. Binet, M.A.	124.533	124.667	29.981	25.886	4.469	3.859	5.905	Control .134	.0227	.008
2. Binet, I.Q.	102.911	103.156	19.079	20.669	2.844	3.081	4.193	Control .245	.0584	.02
3. Binet, C.A. (45 prs. subjects)	123.111	123.067	25.314	25.565	3.774	3.811	5.363	Experimental .044	.0082	.0029
B. Test Results										
1. Reading—Paragraph Meaning	39.067	41.733	28.520	27.786	4.252	4.142	5.936	Control 2.666	.4491	.16
2. Reading—Sentence Meaning	24.667	27.089	17.315	19.687	2.581	2.935	3.908	Control 2.422	.6198	.22
3. Reading—Word Meaning	28.422	29.933	21.437	20.472	3.196	3.052	4.419	Control 1.511	.3410	.12
4. Reading—Total	92.378	98.756	64.829	65.921	9.664	9.827	13.783	Control 6.378	.4627	.17
5. Arithmetic—Computation	73.511	78.667	35.551	35.517	5.300	5.295	7.492	Control 5.156	.6882	.25

Test	Mean of Stutterers	Mean of Control Group	S.D. of Distribution of Stutterers	S.D. of Distribution of Controls	S.D. of Mean of Stutterers	S.D. of Mean of Controls	S.D. of Diff. of Means	Difference Obtained	Ratio of Diff. to S.D. of Diff. of Means	Experimental Coefficient
6. Arithmetic—Reasoning	42.756	45.689	26.770	30.199	3.991	4.502	6.016	Control 2.933	.4875	.18
7. Arithmetic—Total	116.267	124.356	60.600	63.080	9.034	9.404	13.040	Control 8.089	.6230	.22
8. Spelling	72.667	78.089	47.529	51.233	7.085	7.638	10.418	Control 5.422	.5204	.19
9. Accomplishment Quotient	100.0	103.068	12.636	12.668	1.913	1.910	2.703	Control 3.068	1.1342	.408
IV. Woodworth-Cady, Woodworth-Matthews Questionnaire										
A. Equating Groups										
1. Binet, M.A.	124.415	124.3085	26.345	26.745				Experimental .1065		
2. Binet, I.Q.	100.9045	101.33	19.870	20.085				Control .4255		
B. Psychotic Responses (46 and 47 prs. subjects)	22.6522	20.1304	9.616	9.9532	1.4179	1.4676	2.0406	Experimental 2.5218	1.2357	.44

Test	Mean of Stutterers	Mean of Control Group	S.D. of Distribution of Stutterers	S.D. of Distribution of Controls	S.D. of Mean of Stutterers	S.D. of Mean of Controls	S.D. of Diff. of Means	Difference Obtained	Ratio of Diff. to S.D. of Diff. of Means	Experimental Coefficient
V. Kent-Rosanoff Free Association Test (41 prs. subjects)										
A. Equating Groups								Experimental		
1. Binet, M.A.	122.135	121.645	27.30	28.92	4.2636	4.517	6.219	.49	.0788	.0283
2. Binet, I.Q.	100.55	101.16	17.31	19.22	2.703	3.002	4.039	Control .61	.15103	.054
B. Test Results										
1. Total Reaction Times										
a. Mid-scores	2.8951	2.6951	1.164	.9228	.1818	.1441	.232	.2	Exp. .86207	.310
b. Quartile (upper) ..	4.6878	4.1415	2.3064	1.529	.3602	.2388	.4322	.5463	Exp. 1.264	.455
2. Qualitative Responses										
a. Common	69.2075	70.427	22.13	21.415	3.4562	3.345	4.8096	1.2195	Control .2536	.091
b. Doubtful	5.2317	4.256	4.0606	3.707	.6342	.5789	.8586	.9756	Exp. 1.1363	.409
c. Individual	25.6075	25.305	20.623	21.555	3.221	3.3664	4.6588	.3655	Exp. .07845	.0282
VI. Physical Traits										
A. Equating Groups (38 prs. subjects)										
M.A.	121.7105	122.3685	27.035	27.73						
C.A.	120.7895	120.5265	26.035	27.66						

Test	Mean of Stutterers	Mean of Control Group	S.D. of Distribution of Stutterers	S.D. of Distribution of Controls	S.D. of Mean of Stutterers	S.D. of Mean of Controls	S.D. of Diff. of Means	Difference Obtained	Ratio of Diff. to S.D. of Diff. of Means	Experimental Coefficient
B. Results										
1. Weight	73.158	69.4735	20.59	18.265	3.34	2.963	4.465	3.6845	.8252	.3
2. Height	54.1824	53.8158	4.572	4.719	.7417	.7656	1.066	.3684	.3456	.12
3. Chest Girth, Inspiration	27.8158	27.5	2.597	3.035	.4213	.4924	.6481	.3158	.4873	.18
4. Chest Girth, Expiration	25.7631	25.6053	2.602	2.954	.4221	.4792	.6386	.1578	.2471	.09
5. Lung Capacity	112.2295	109.7975	32.18	28.98	5.29	4.76	7.116	2.432	.3418	.12
6. Heart Rate	102.763	99.4735	15.215	15.065	2.468	2.444	3.474	3.2895	.9409	.34
7. Blood Pressure (Systolic)	95.076	93.409	12.62	10.405	2.197	1.8110	2.847	1.667	.5855	.21
8. Blood Pressure (Diastolic)	63.106	65.076	12.045	8.80	2.097	1.532	2.597	1.970	.7585	.27
9. Strength of Grip, Right Arm	39.342	39.6055	13.25	12.495	2.15	2.027	2.955	.2635	.0892	.03
10. Strength of Grip, Left Arm	37.6315	37.3685	14.53	12.165	2.357	1.974	3.074	.2630	.0586	.03
VII. Speech Test										
A. Equating Groups (33 prs. subjects)										
I.Q.	99.621	101.1365	16.19	18.06				1.5155		
M.A.	123.8635	124.7725	26.975	28.045				.9090		

BIBLIOGRAPHY

1. SCRIPTURE, E. W. *Stuttering and Lisping.* Macmillan (1923 edition).
2. BORDEN, R. C., and BUSSE, A. C. *Speech Correction.* F. S. Crofts & Co., New York, 1925.
3. BLUEMEL, C. S. *Stammering and Cognate Defects of Speech,* Vol. 1, G. E. Stechert, New York, 1913.
4. MAKUEN, G. HUDSON. "A Brief History of the Treatment of Stammering." *Philadelphia Medical Journal,* Vol. XIII, 1909-10, pp. 191-97.
5. FLETCHER, J. M. "An Experimental Study of Stuttering." *American Journal of Psychology,* Vol. XXV, April, 1914, pp. 201-55.
6. BLANTON, M. G. and S. *Speech Training for Children.* Century, 1920.
7. BAGBY, ENGLISH. *Lectures on Psychology of Personality.* (Multigraphed) Whitlock's Book Store, Inc., New Haven, Conn.
8. DUNLAP, KNIGHT. "The Stuttering Boy." *Journal of Abnormal Psychology,* Vol. 12, 1917, pp. 44-48.
9. McCALL, W. A. *How to Experiment in Education.* Macmillan, 1923.
10. BLANTON, SMILEY. "A Survey of Speech Defects." *Journal of Educational Psychology,* Vol. 7, Dec., 1916, p. 580.
11. McCALL, W. A. *How to Measure in Education.* Macmillan, 1922.
12. WALLIN, J. E. WALLACE. "A Census of Speech Defects." *School and Society,* Vol. 3, Feb. 5, 1916, p. 213.
13. CONRADI, EDWARD. "Speech Development in the Child." *Pedagogical Seminar,* Vol. 11, p. 382.
14. ROOT, A. R. "A Survey of Speech Defectives in the Public Elementary Schools of South Dakota." *Elementary School Journal,* Vol. 26, p. 531.
15. ROOT, A. R. "Special Education and the Speech Defective." *Educational Administration and Supervision,* Vol. 13, p. 255.
16. TERMAN, L. M., et al. *Genetic Studies of Genius,* Vol. 1. Stanford University, 1925.
17. MATTHEWS, E. "A Study of Emotional Stability in Children." *The Journal of Delinquency,* Vol. 8, Jan., 1923, pp. 1-40.
18. YULE, G. W. *An Introduction to the Theory of Statistics.* Charles Griffin & Co., Ltd., London.
19. ROSANOFF, A. J. *Manual of Psychiatry.* John Wiley, New York (1927 edition).
20. WOOD, T. D., and ROWELL, H. G. *Health Supervision and Medical Inspection of Schools.* Saunders, Philadelphia, 1921.
21. BALLARD, P. B. "Sinistrality and Speech." *Journal of Experimental Pedagogy,* Vol. 1, p. 298.
22. TERMAN, L. M. *Hygiene of the School Child.* Houghton Mifflin, 1914.
23. STARLING, E. H. *Principles of Human Physiology.* Lea and Febiger, Philadelphia, 1926 (4th edition).